The Most Beautiful
Thing in the World
and other poems

The Most Beautiful Thing in the World

and other poems

Micheal D. Winterburn

Illustrated by Dave Hill

Matador
9 Priory Business Park,
Wistow Road, Kibworth Beauchamp,
Leicestershire. LE8 0RX
Tel: 0116 279 2299
Email: books@troubador.co.uk
Web: www.troubador.co.uk/matador
Twitter: @matadorbooks

ISBN 978 1838591 366

British Library Cataloguing in Publication Data.
A catalogue record for this book is available from the British Library.

Printed and bound in the UK by TJ International, Padstow, Cornwall
Typeset in 11pt Sabon MT by Troubador Publishing Ltd, Leicester, UK

Matador is an imprint of Troubador Publishing Ltd

To Jeremy, Kate, Jude and Aletha

Contents

A Hearty Welcome!

O how wonderful to meet you!
I've been sent along to greet you!
And if you follow me inside
I'll be your very special guide!

You'll notice just how well we're dressed,
With rhymes and titles neatly pressed;
Our words scrubbed up to help them shine,
Our sentences all in a line.

You'll find our spellings are correct,
And all our punctuation checked.
Now, if you're fine with how we look,
Perhaps you'd like to read our book?

Do come on in and have some fun –
There's merriment for everyone!
But let me say this from the start,
That some of us may touch your heart.

For life will have you laugh, or cry,
Or jump for joy, or say goodbye;
And we are poems that like to show
Emotions you may come to know.

I Met a Goat

I met a goat
  Beside a gate;
  Her name was Kate,
She ate my coat.

So I was cross.
  I said, 'That's crass!
  What's wrong with grass?!'
She said, 'It's gross!'

Kate wasn't shy:
  She grabbed my shoe
  And ate that, too!
Then gulped my tie!

I locked the goat
  Inside the gate
  And said to Kate,
  'I hope the coat
    The cross
    The crass
    The grass
    The gross
    The shy
    The shoe
    The too
    The tie
All make you sick
  And make you cry!
  Goodbye!'

3

Great Grandma's Mobility Scooter

Great Grandma rides a scooter, and it's heaven for her feet.
It's a flashy double-decker and it speeds along the street.
There's room for seven downstairs, but can squeeze a couple more,
While upstairs there's a juice bar with a bouncer on the door!

It takes up all the pavement as she races to the shops,
So stand aside or go and hide – or go and call the cops!
Her friends hang from the windows and operate their drones,
To frighten off the seagulls stealing children's ice cream cones.

Great Grandma packs her purchases inside the scooter's boot,
Then off she zooms back home again, but takes a different route.
'Cos every single seagull that's been bothered by a drone
Will try to dive-bomb Grandma with some 'ice cream' of their own!

Ballerina

See the lady
How she dances
Light and free
  She floats and twirls.

See her smiling
Very pretty
In her flounces
  And her curls.

Now she stretches
Tall on tiptoe
Reaches up
  To touch the sky.

All her body
Plays the music
Of a lovely
  Lullaby.

Watch Out for Cats!

The feeders are full! The feeders are full!
Seeds, fat balls and refreshing water.
Bread strewn about on the ground.

Watch out for cats! Watch out for cats!
Look left, look right, look up, look down!
Peck at the fat ball.
Look left, look right!
Peck at the seeds.
Peck at the seeds.
Peck at the seeds.
Look up, look down!
Watch out for cats! Watch out for cats!

Big bully blackbird barging in!
Big belly to fill.
Fly around. Come back later.
First to arrive, now at the back.
Don't eat it all! Don't eat it all!
Wait until he's gone.
Watch out for cats! Watch out for cats!
Look up, look down, look left, look right!

Safe to return. Safe to return.
Peck at the seeds.
Peck at the fat ball.
Peck at the fat ball.
Peck at the fat ball.
Look right, look right, look left, look left!
Watch out for cats! Watch out for cats!

Little Boulders

Every single morning,
 No matter what I do,
I guarantee a little stone
 Will jump into my shoe!

Though the stones are tiny,
 They feel so very big,
And once these boulders touch my toes
 They then begin to dig!

With every step I take,
 I grimace with the pain,
Yet when I empty out my shoe
 One more jumps in again!

I wore my wellies once,
 To keep the stones at bay,
But clearly they can pole-vault, yeah,
 'Cos three got in that day!

I took another route,
 To foil their fiendish tricks,
Yet even then they ambushed me,
 And ouch! they felt like bricks!

Do they lie in waiting?
 Are all invasions planned?
What have I done to anger them?
 I just don't understand!

The Adventures of a Pound

I was born seven years ago within the Royal Mint,
A bonny baby pound with a healthy golden glint.
Since then I've been about a bit and seen a thing or two,
And because you show an interest I'll tell you of a few.
I've been hidden in a cupboard in a jar meant for jam,
Scrutinised by foreigners who wonder what I am,
Stowed away for days on end in hot, stuffy purses,
Handled with the caring touch of doctors and nurses,
Tossed high into the air with a mighty thumb flick
That spun me round and round feeling dizzy and sick.
I once went to Spain but it wasn't much fun:
I spent a week locked in a safe and never saw the sun.
I've been dropped into a bottle for a charitable cause,
Given in part payment for some dirty household chores.
I plopped into a gutter as we sprinted for a bus,
Was discovered not long after by a lad who made a fuss.
I've been swopped for tobacco and for cinema seats,
Diddled with and fiddled with by far too many cheats.
I've resided in the mansions of a magnate and a lord,
Purchased bread and butter – all the mother could afford.
A young girl gave me gladly for a birthday gift of scent,
I was shot at by a pistol and sustained a nasty dent.
I've travelled all the railway tracks and all the major roads,
Been wrapped up in a hanky (not the nicest of abodes).
I was flung into a pool for a swimmer to retrieve,
Refused in a nightclub and politely asked to leave.
I've been kissed and cuddled heartily when won in a bet,
Parted with reluctantly when paying off a debt.
I've led a very busy life, yet I try not to complain;
It's really just as well, because . . . I'll do it all again!

Summer Holidays

Off we run,
In the sun,
  Singing as we go,
In our summer holidays,
  How we love them so.

Stride a stream,
In a dream,
  Watch the waters flow,
In our summer holidays,
  How we love them so.

Scale a wall,
Ten feet tall,
  Where the mosses grow,
In our summer holidays,
  How we love them so.

Climb a tree,
Wild and free,
  Feel the breezes blow,
In our summer holidays,
  How we love them so.

Chase a fly
Through the sky,
    Yelling at our foe,
In our summer holidays,
    How we love them so.

Play a game,
Call her name,
    Searching high and low,
In our summer holidays,
    How we love them so.

Time for tea,
Home we flee,
    Laughing as we go,
In our summer holidays,
    How we love them so.
In our summer holidays,
    O how we love them so!

Eat Up Your Greens!

Eat up your greens or you'll soon fall to bits,
Those who refuse are just silly old twits!
Pizzas and pies are both fine in their place,
But don't keep on stuffing them into your face!
Please make some room for a carrot or two,
You know fruit and veg are essential for you!
Eat beetroots, bananas, try parsnips and peas,
From underground, on the ground, hanging from trees.
Some are best roasted or just eaten raw,
Boil them or steam them – then have a few more!
Raise up a body that's healthy and strong,
Or live with regret when it starts to go wrong!
A sturdy new building needs iron and bricks,
It will sway and collapse made with cardboard and sticks!
So make a decision and get this thing right:
Reach for some cabbage or cauli tonight!

What Are You Doing?

Mix, mix, mix, mix,
Stir, stir, stir, stir . . .
'What are you doing, Father?'
'A moment! – I'm baking!'

Knock, knock, knock, knock,
Bang, bang, bang, bang . . .
'What are you doing, Mother?'
'A moment! – I'm mending!'

'One, two, three, four,
Five, six, seven, eight …'
'What are you doing, Sister?'
'A moment! – I'm counting!'

'Doh, ray, me, fah,
Soh, lah, te, doh …'
'What are you doing, Brother?'
'A moment! – I'm singing!'

'Howl, howl, howl, howl,
Wail, wail, wail, wail …'
'What are you doing, Son?'
'What are you doing, Brother?'
'A moment! – I'm crying!'

Could this be the world's shortest poem?
Quite possibly. I can't think how another
poem could be shorter. But shouldn't a
very short poem have a very short title,
too? Quite possibly. Don't forget, however,
that a very short poem leaves a heck of a
lot of white space on a page and many readers
might think they're not getting value for
money if they see a page that's about 98%
empty. But surely, in that case, they'd print
more than just one poem on the page? Hmm,
possibly. However, even if this isn't the
world's shortest poem, it might qualify as
the poem with the world's longest title.
Ideally, I suppose, it would be the world's
shortest poem that also has the world's
longest title. That would be really
something, eh? It would, yes – but how long
do you think it would be before someone
else comes along and beats it, steals your
glory? Hmm, I hadn't thought of that.
Anyway, after such a very long title as
this, the very short poem had better
be worth it, hadn't it? I suppose so. Does it
rhyme? Oh, yes, it's a perfect rhyme. Is it
clever? Well, I at least think so. I hope you
do, too. So can we get on with it, then? I
suppose so. We'd better do, hadn't we? Yes!
(Sorry, I'll shut up now.) Thank you! Phew!

Atishoo!

A tissue!

14

The Black Hole Monster

I suck and I suck with all of my might,
I gobble up planets, I gorge upon light!
I greedily, speedily pounce upon all,
So stay well away or you'll stumble and fall!
And as you are zooming towards my insides
I'll take you on hideous, giddyous rides!
I'll grab you and twist you and stretch you with ease,
And pull you apart like a long string of cheese!
Then I'll munch you and crunch you and spread you about,
You'll be in me forever, I won't spit you out!
There's no other monster as fearsome as me,
I'm the biggest, the baddest, that ever will be!
Now I bet you are wondering where everything goes:
Well, that is *my* secret – and NOBODY knows!

Naughty Little Spider

Oh, you naughty little spider,
  You gave me such a fright!
You crept out of my pillowcase,
  Now I won't sleep tonight!

You've been crawling on my ceiling,
  Please use the floor instead!
Don't wave eight hairy, scary legs,
  Don't dangle from a thread!

Stop weaving webs around our house,
  You haven't paid us rent!
Stop catching flies for spider pies –
  I think it's time you went!

Why such a hullabaloo?
It's making me feel so blue!
I'm a creature just like you,
But I do what *spiders* do!

Now there's no doubt that it's true,
I've a lot of legs on view,
Whereas you have only two,
Which really is far too few:
It's a shame some never grew!

If my rent is overdue,
Then take me to court and sue.
It's free to live in a zoo,
So that should give you a clue!

This talk about pies is poo!
I cover the flies in goo,
And it turns them into stew,
So they're easier to chew.

Our discussion is now through.
Do stop telling me to shoo,
'Cos I'm staying put – so BOO!

Bouncy Bouncy

I've lost my ball,
It jumped the wall,
It bashed the cat and made her fall!

My bouncy, bouncy,
Bouncy, bouncy
Ball goes up and down.
Bouncy, bouncy,
Bouncy, bouncy,
All around the town!

It's broken free,
And as you'll see,
It's bouncing rather recklessly!

My bouncy, bouncy,
Bouncy, bouncy
Ball goes up and down.
Bouncy, bouncy,
Bouncy, bouncy,
Clumsy like a clown!

So guard your nose,
Protect your toes,
Beware those bouncy, bouncy blows!

My bouncy, bouncy,
Bouncy, bouncy
Ball goes up and down.
Bouncy, bouncy,
Bouncy, bouncy,
Scaring half the town!

Limericks

A man on a mission to Mars
Got stuck in a tangle of stars,
   In just under two hours
   They turned into flowers,
So he took them back home in a vase.

I knew a potato that frowned
At the life that he led underground,
   When munched by a worm
   He would wriggle and squirm,
And his screams could be heard miles around.

A woman with warts on her nose,
And blisters and boils on her toes,
   Said, 'Oh, how they hurt,
   And some of them squirt
Twice as far as a fireman's hose!'

An elephant with a short trunk,
Said, 'Goodness me, how it has shrunk!
  In the river I dipped it
  And a crocodile clipped it,
What a dangerous place for a dunk!'

A lady who liked a nice hat
Was hit on the head by a cat;
  It lost one of its lives,
  But now the cat thrives
As her headwear of choice – fancy that!

There was a young man from Montrose
Who said, 'Limericks get right up my nose;
  They at first make me wheeze,
  Then soon after I sneeze,
And I shake from my head to my toes!'

A man who loved golden brown toast
Was offered a slice by his host,
　　But he sneered and he said,
　　'This is merely hot bread!
My toast is a ghost – at the most!'

A jockey too big for his horse
Was told to cut out chocolate sauce,
　　But he smothered his plate
　　And quadrupled his weight,
So the horse now rides *him* round the course!

A contortionist knows, without doubt,
All the dangers of twisting about;
　　Tie a knot, then bend up
　　And you're bound to end up
Back to front, upside down, inside out!

Word Went Round

One day, a man of gentle fed a bird of dickie some
very tasty treats. Word went round, and soon his garden
was filled with ins of rob, lings of star, pies of mag,
rows of spar, daws of jack, and many, many other kinds
of birds of dickie. The man of gentle gave them all some
very tasty treats.

   Happy birds of dickie!

Word went round, and soon thousands of crawlies of creepy
came along to get some tasty treats from the man of gentle.
First came pillars of cater, followed by wigs of ear, hoppers
of grass, pedes of centi, fish of silver, long legs of daddy,
and many, many other kinds of crawlies of creepy. But
the greedy birds of dickie saw them and ate them all up.

   Naughty birds of dickie!

Word went round, and hundreds of cats of pussy came
along, to eat up all the birds of dickie. There were bies
of tab, bays of Bom, dolls of rag, chillas of chin, shells of
tortoise, hairs of short, and many, many other kinds of cats
of pussy. Many of them were cats of tom. But the birds of
dickie were too quick for the cats of pussy and flew away.

   Slowcoach cats of pussy!

Word went round, and all the neighbourhood wows of bow came along, to chase away the cats of pussy. There were ghans of af, huahuas of chi, oodles of p, hunds of dachs, matians of dal, dors of labra, russells of jack, and many, many more kinds of wows of bow. But the cats of pussy jumped up into the trees where the wows of bow couldn't get them.

Clever cats of pussy!

Word went round, and all the owners of dog came along to take their wows of bow home. There were people of old, people of young, people of tall, people of small, people of happy, people of grumpy, and many, many more kinds of owners of dog. But the wows of bow ran between their legs and raced round and round and the owners of dog couldn't catch them.

Naughty wows of bow!

Word went round, and all the bies of bob in the town came
along, to remove everyone from the garden of the man
of gentle. There were police of slim, police of stout, police
of hairy, police of jolly, police of stern, and many, many
other kinds of bies of bob. The bies of bob said that all
the wows of bow would be arrested and locked up
if they didn't go home straightaway. So the
wows of bow *did* go home.

    Brave bies of bob!

The next day, the man of gentle ate up all the very tasty treats
himself.

    Wise man of gentle!

Autumn Leaves

The autumn leaves are turning yellow;
That's because the year is mellow.

The autumn leaves are turning red;
A scene of beauty overhead.

The autumn leaves are turning pink;
A lovely spectacle, I think.

The autumn leaves are turning brown;
Before too long they'll all fall down.

The autumn leaves are turning blue;
I'm not sure that's what they should do.

The autumn leaves are turning green;
Now going back to where they've been?

The autumn leaves are turning white;
There's something here that isn't right!

The autumn leaves are turning black;
Should Mother Nature get the sack?

Rhyme Rhyme

'Rhyme, rhyme,
All the time;
It's sad,
It's bad,
It's driving me mad,
It's the worst affliction I've ever had,
When I'm finally cured I'll be ever so glad!'

'No you won't!'

'Yes I will, yes I will,
It's making me ill,
I've had my full fill,
And I'm really in need of a de-rhyming pill!
Or this rhyme,
All the time,
Could potentially kill!'

'No it couldn't!'

'Well, remember what I've said
If I suddenly drop d – '

'Yoohoo! Still here! Only joking!'

'Told you!'

Kitty La Puss

This is the story of Kitty La Puss,
Who shrinks from all contact and cannot stand fuss.
Stay clear of her whiskers, just *don't* touch her fur,
Prepare for a snarl when expecting a purr.

For Kitty has battled, she's fought with her claws;
Her body is battered and covered in sores.
Her life has been troubled, her times have been tough,
And goodness knows Kitty has suffered enough.

She was born in a house that was lacking in care,
And while still a kitten was kicked out of there.
Feeble and hungry, and motherless now,
She had to survive, but she didn't know how.

Other cats mauled her – there were scratches and bites.
Many dogs caught her – there were terrible fights.
Her fur was pulled out and both ears were torn,
And Kitty would lie in the blood that was drawn.

She got stuck in a wall and couldn't get out,
So a boy yanked her tail and it knocked her about.
Her jaw was all broken, her mouth was a mess,
She shivered and cried in her state of distress.

Two men followed Kitty, with dogs in a pack,
They tried to throw Kitty inside a big sack.
She shot up a tree and in terror clung tight,
And feared for her life throughout most of the night.

Poor Kitty is angry, her manners are wild;
She needs tender love, as you'd give to a child.
There's no one to feed her, or give her a bed,
She's lost and abandoned and almost half-dead.

Think kindly of Kitty, of Kitty La Puss,
But do not approach her, nor make any fuss;
For Kitty is now far beyond human aid:
Her past and her future are already made.

Or tell me I'm wrong, that I must change my mind;
That perhaps, if we're gentle and patient and kind,
We can rescue poor Kitty, no more will she roam,
She'll be safe and secure in a loving new home.

Three of Us
(A True Story)

We found it in the river while fishing.
About four inches high,
It had a fat, bulb-like base
With a slim neck widening to a broad brim.
It was flaky, brittle, a dull gold.
Ancient, we thought.
A Roman vase, without doubt.

We forgot the fishing,
Took the vase to my house,
Wrapped it gently in a pillowcase
And placed it at the back of a drawer:
Safe for the next day,
When Mr Sanderson would marvel
At our glorious find.

The three of us guarded it
All the way to school.
We kept curious eyes away from it,
Were careful not to damage it.
But at the school gates
A huge crowd gathered round.
We had to admit having treasure.

Everyone gasped and we loved it.
Power and importance were ours.
The whole school followed us.
Mr Sanderson, the headmaster,
Studied it for only five seconds,
Turned it the other way round, and said,
'A doorknob. An old-fashioned brass doorknob.'

Three of us felt a bit stupid.

Ginger Biscuits

'You need to come away from that tin, now, you've had enough.'

'Soon.'

'You're being greedy.'

'Just one more.'

'You said that five biscuits ago.'

'Four.'

'Four, then. But you'd already had eight.'

'Seven.'

'Seven, then. Carry on as you are and you'll be sick; I've told you.'

'No I won't.'

'You're six years old. Your stomach isn't big enough.'

'There's room for more.'

'So go ahead and find out. Learn a lesson.'

'I love ginger biscuits.'

'So do I, but there won't be any left! I only bought them this morning. Why are you still messing about in the kitchen? I bet the tin's empty now, isn't it?'

'No – I've just filled it up again.'

'Yuk!'

Complaint

Dear God
or Mother Nature
or Evolution
or Whoever is *Really* in Charge,

I'm complaining.

I'm just fed up. Twice a day, every day,
morning and night, my mum or my dad
stands over me to make sure I brush
my teeth properly.

'Don't argue,' Dad says, 'just do it,
or they'll all turn green and fall out,
one by one, like apples from a tree.
One day you'll be thankful.'

Well, I'm not thankful. I'm annoyed!
Are you paying attention?! I thought
us human beings were supposed to be
your best creation? The tops? But we're not!
You haven't designed us properly!
You must have been half-asleep!

Sharks are horrible and go around
biting everything they see – with a big
stupid grin on their face! But *they* get
unlimited teeth! If one falls out, another
one grows. Always. Forever!

I have *never* bitten off someone's head
or legs, yet I have to brush and brush and brush.
Two sets only! Where's the fairness in that?
Sharks deserve to be toothless, not me.
Why don't *they* have to brush?!

And while we're on the subject, if we could
still swing through trees we'd get to school
a lot faster, and it would be far more fun.
You didn't think of that, did you!

And maybe if we'd been born with a pouch,
like a kangaroo, we wouldn't need to carry
a school bag. We wouldn't need pockets or purses
or handbags or sporrans. Save a fortune!
Perhaps that slipped your mind, too!

Oh, and then there's . . .

Giggleghost

At a mansion in the forest,
    Where travellers spend the night,
A little ghost was sent to work,
    To give them all a fright.

This was his first time on the job,
    He wasn't very keen,
He'd lately left spook-training school,
    Which taught him to be mean.

Well, he jumped down from the rafters,
    And landed on a bed,
Then in a voice that shook the house
    He menacingly said:

'Giggle, giggle, giggle,
    Ha ha ha,
I'll frighten your socks off,
    Whoever you are!

Giggle, giggle, giggle,
    Ho ho ho,
Please put them on again,
    I'm joking, you know!'

The man who occupied the bed
    Just laughed and laughed and laughed,
'If you believe I'm scared,' said he,
    'You must be pretty daft.'

The other ghosts went up the wall,
    They all were seeing red,
The little ghost had let them down,
    And this is what they said:

'A ghost should rattle heavy chains,
    A ghost should wail and moan,
Yet all you do is laugh, laugh, laugh,
    No wonder we all groan!'

The little ghost could not agree,
    He had to shake his head,
He faced the elder bogey men,
    And this is what he said:

'Giggle, giggle, giggle,
    Hee hee hee,
Frightening their socks off
    Just isn't for me.

I cannot be ghoulish,
    That's just mad!
But, in particular,
    I cannot be bad!'

The elder ghosts were not impressed
    By his explanation,
They quit the house and went elsewhere,
    In exasperation.

The little ghost was left alone
    To haunt in his own style,
Travellers heard about his gift
    And came to stay awhile.

The little ghost's great sense of fun
    Delighted them no end;
They didn't see him as a ghost,
    But as a valued friend.

Travellers laying weary bones
    Upon a restful bed,
Looked forward to their night-time laugh,
    For this is what he said:

'Giggle, giggle, giggle,
    Ha ha ha,
I'll frighten your socks off,
    Whoever you are!

Giggle, giggle, giggle,
    Ho ho ho,
Please put them on again,
    I'm joking, you know!'

Bumpty Dumpty

When I was very little, Mum took an egg from the fridge
and walked it across the table as if it had legs.

She put on a silly, singing voice: 'La di da di da, I'm on my
way to the shops, I need to cross the road. La di da di da.'

She took the salt and pepper and some other things
and made them into a row of shops. 'And this is the road,'
she said, laying a folded tea towel across the table.

'Little egg! Little egg! Watch out for all the traffic going by!
At the kerb – halt! Look left. Look right. Look left again.
If the road is clear, quick march, but don't run.'

An egg cup, in my mother's hand, came whizzing by,
with suitable car sounds. Then a sauce bottle flew past
from the opposite direction.

The silly voice again: 'I'm a clever egg. I don't need
to stop and look. That's for other eggs, not me!
Eeeeaaaaooooowwww! A very fast car is coming!'

Splat! Yolk and albumen went everywhere. On me. On Mum.
On the dog – who sniffed at it, then licked it up.

'That was Bumpty Dumpty, Humpty's little sister. You are
as fragile as an egg. That broken egg could be you. *Always* take
care on the roads. Don't be a *Numpty* Dumpty!'

Ever since, whenever I approach a kerb, I become an egg.
And stop!

From Shoes to Shoes
(In more than ten steps)

Shoes have laces;
Laces look like string;
String can tie things up;
Up in the sky there are clouds;
Clouds are made from water;
Water can be used to make coffee;
Coffee is made from beans;
Beans are tasty on toast;
Toast is bread when it burns;
Burns can be caused by fire;
Fire can be started by matches;
Matches are sold in boxes;
So are shoes.

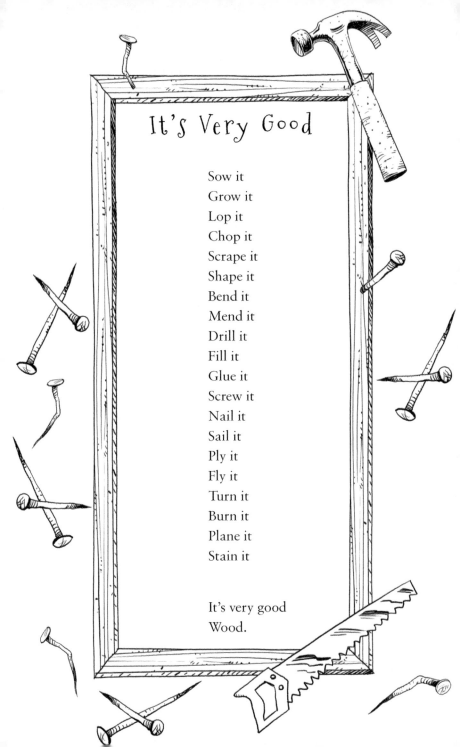

It's Very Good

Sow it
Grow it
Lop it
Chop it
Scrape it
Shape it
Bend it
Mend it
Drill it
Fill it
Glue it
Screw it
Nail it
Sail it
Ply it
Fly it
Turn it
Burn it
Plane it
Stain it

It's very good
Wood.

Bubblegum Billy

Bubblegum Billy, the bubblegum kid,
Blew bubblegum bubbles in all that he did;
Bubbles with his breakfast, bubbles with his tea,
His mother couldn't stop him, nor could we.

Bubblegum Billy, the bubblegum boy,
Said bubble-blowing was an absolute joy.
His bubbles were of yellow, of green and red and blue,
His father couldn't stop him, nor could you.

Bubblegum Billy, the bubblegum lad,
Was led to the doctor's to find out what he had.
Severe bubblitis was developing fast,
The doctor couldn't cure it, but said it wouldn't last.

Bubblegum Billy, the bubblegum champ,
Blew bubbles in the scout hut, bubbles in the camp,
Bubbles on the roundabouts, bubbles on the slides,
No one there could stop him, nor anyone besides.

Bubblegum Billy, the bubblegum king,
Blew bubbles in the classroom when it was time to sing,
Bubbles in the playground, bubbles in the hall,
His teachers couldn't stop him, nor anyone at all.

Bubblegum Billy, the bubblegum loon,
One night blew a bubble as big as the moon;
The bubble tugged at Billy and pulled him off the ground,
His parents didn't see him, they never heard a sound.

Bubblegum Billy, the bubblegum freak,
Flew high into the sky and hit a mountain peak;
The bubble burst and Billy fell, as if attached to weights,
But Billy's blowing bubbles still, within the Pearly Gates.

Flying Things

I walk through the fields.
All alone.
Feeling pretty bored.
Wondering what to do.
I'm tired because I'm bored.
My eyelids droop and I yawn.
So I lie down for a little nap.
There's nothing else to do.

Then suddenly!
I am

High up among the flying things,
Where I have beak and tail and wings
And eagle eyes and taloned feet:
A bird in every way complete.

I swoop and soar, just as I please,
    To test my aerobatic skills;
I skim the leafy tops of trees,
    Perform a dozen other drills.

I rush through valleys, over lakes,
Wherever my new fancy takes;
I circle towns, where fumes and smoke
Assault my eyes and make me choke.

But as I fly dark storm-clouds growl,
    Rain spears down to stab at me,
Wind bares its fangs and with a howl
    It chases me relentlessly.

I search for shelter in the trees
    And, noticing that I have fled,
    A kestrel hovers overhead
And boasts because he flies with ease.

On branches, as the torrents stop,
    Rain globules fatten, big and round;
They drip and drop and fall and flop
    And spatter on the sodden ground.

Ah! Now the clouds, as they unfold,
Reveal a ball of blazing gold;
So off again I flap and fly,
To join a rainbow in the sky.

Then suddenly the air is dark
  With every kind of flying thing,
And blackbird, sparrow, starling, lark,
  Enjoy new warmth and start to sing.

A helicopter comes to slice
  A channel through the busy air,
And all are scattered in a trice,
  Feathers and fury everywhere!

Ten parachutes start to descend;
Soon, saddened that their flight must end,
The human pendulums beneath
Will meet the ground with gritted teeth.

Above me floats a huge balloon,
   And as its basket gently rocks
   The travellers within the box
Enjoy their lazy afternoon.

Jet planes pass in close formation,
Here to give a demonstration;
They loop the loop then onward sail,
Leaving a long white vapour trail.

A star-bound rocket thunders by,
Blasting flame at frightened sky,
With lightning speed it hurtles high.

A kite jumps up, to dance and twirl,
The plaything of a distant girl.
A model plane is on patrol,
But plummets as it tries to roll.

Now I fear that *I* am ailing,
For I find my wings are failing;
I'm tumbling, tumbling, from the skies,
Down, down, to where my body lies.

I open my eyes.
Walk back through the fields.
Not too bored any more.
A little spring in my step.
Soon be home.

To the Rhythm and the Beat

Let's dance to the beat,
To the rhythm and the beat,
To the rhythm,
To the rhythm,
To the rhythm and the beat.

Abandon your seat,
Feel the music in your feet,
Feel the music,
Feel the music,
Feel the music in your feet.

Join us in the street,
There is magic in your feet,
There is magic,
There is magic,
There is magic in your feet.

O isn't life sweet,
When you boogie to the beat,
When you boogie,
When you boogie,
When you boogie to the beat.

So dance to the beat,
To the rhythm and the beat,
To the rhythm,
To the rhythm,
To the rhythm and the beat.

Give us rhythm,
Lots of rhythm,
Love the rhythm and the beat.

Sister Witches

Hagatha, Nagatha and Bagatha, we
Are old sister witches, one, two, three.
We've long hook noses and pointed chins,
Bony white fingers and legs like pins.
Our eyes are yellow and as bright as an owl's,
We frighten the world with our sinister scowls.
Lizards and toads make their homes in our hats
And the folds of our cloaks conceal black cats!

We dance in the twilight around a great fire,
With the stench of our potions polluting the shire.
Into the cauldron drop dragonfly wings,
Slug slime, dog lips and jellyfish stings,
Large lumps of gristle and big blobs of fat
And lots of really horrible things like that.
While we watch our concoctions bubble and swell
We cackle and screech and cast a spell!

But as soon as the moonlight shadows fall
We snatch our broomsticks from the wall,
And with wicked sniggers and whoops of joy
Cry warnings to every girl and boy,
'Watch out! Awful Hagatha's on the prowl;
Quick run! Nasty Nagatha's deeds are foul;
Take cover! Bad Bagatha's eyeing your door;
We're coming! We're coming! We'll get you, for sure!'

Cambridge Ducks

Cambridge ducks need safety helmets,
Cambridge ducks are under attack!
Cambridge ducks are always dodging
Poles that threaten them with a big whack!
Whack whack,
Whack whack.
Quack quack,
Quack quack.

Cambridge punts are packed with people,
Cambridge punts are never slack!
Cambridge punts are very noisy,
With oohs! and aahs! and yackety-yak!
Yak yak,
Yak yak.
Quack quack,
Quack quack.

Cambridge ducks adore free titbits,
Cambridge ducks will chase a snack!
Cambridge ducks will face all danger,
From wings that break, to heads that crack!
Crack crack,
Crack crack.
Quack quack,
Quack quack.

The Ballad of Mrs Todd

Mrs Todd is the organist
    At Ribley Parish Church,
A peaceful place of worship ringed
    With elm and silver birch.

One Monday morning off she went
    To practise on the keys,
But as she played a soothing tune
    She blasted out a sneeze.

Achoo! Achoo! Achoo! Achoo!
    And one more time, ACHOO!
Her body shook so violently
    It shocked her through and through!

Her eyeballs did a somersault,
    Then blazed with crimson fire,
Her nostrils flared and spouted steam,
    Her hair stood stiff as wire.

She thrashed the keyboards, yanked the stops
    And kicked the pedals hard,
The church mice fled and hid behind
    The trees out in the yard.

The bellows rose, the bellows fell,
　　Loud gusty winds they blew,
The bourdons boomed, the trumpets blared,
　　The flutes all snapped in two.

And as the pipes shook in their ranks
　　Their notes traversed the air,
To cause vibrations in the pews,
　　Vibrations everywhere.

The windows trembled in their frames,
　　The huge door slammed and locked,
The bells rang out, folk wondered why,
　　So to the church they flocked.

The vicar led the curious crowd,
　　They heard the organ's roar,
The verger brought a heavy bar
　　And battered down the door.

Inside they met the strangest scene,
　　As Mrs Todd played on:
The pews were dancing to her tunes,
　　Her music marathon.

The bellows rose to massive size,
Wind whistled down the aisle,
It scooped the people off their feet
And dumped them in a pile.

The vicar prayed for Higher Aid,
While struggling to his knees,
When suddenly old Mrs Todd
Erupted with a sneeze.

Achoo! Achoo! Achoo! ACHOO!
Her body shook again,
And Hallelujah! Mrs Todd
Was now as right as rain.

She flicked a switch, the bellows dropped,
The pipes were all struck dumb,
And peace returned to Ribley Church –
The vicar's Aid had come.

Now, if you go to Ribley Church,
Please do be on your toes:
Should Mrs Todd look set to sneeze,
Be sure to pinch her nose!

Oops!

Yes, oh yes, a terrible mess
    Hit the floor in a spurt
    And my language was curt
    Because boy did it hurt
And it caused me distress!

It was an unfortunate cough,
    So there's no need to blame
    Our good Queen or her aim
    Or the sword for the shame
Of chopping my ear off!

And please do make light of my plight
    When I knelt with head bowed
    Hearing screams from the crowd,
    Since I'm not in a shroud
And am now dubbed a knight!

Hippopotamus

Help me to ungrump and degrumpify,
or I may just overwobble and bigburst
for teenytiny reason. Such a calamitydisaster
would not be healthyhelpful for anybodyone
around, croc or human. Not saying I'm a
dangerphysical, or tryingtoworryyou,
but I am the ownerpossessor of a
greatbigenormousgobcan'tcloseit, and
wheneveralways it gets a chanceportunity
it shoutblasts at a loudloudblimeythat'sloud
full-volume bettercoveryourears.
Then I might bite your leg off, because my
greatbigenormousgobcan'tcloseit does indeed
clampshut from timetotime.

So please, if you really must glide past me
in your canoe, as if you're a davidattenborough,
do help me to cheerlightenup, so I become
a placidcalmy and not a yellystampysplashyintheriver,
'cos that's notaveryprettysighty, especially if
you're also minus a limb. You could start
by telling me a jokefunnyhaha. Then climb on
my back and give it a goodtickleooisn'tthatlovely!
Not much entertainment in a river, so if you do that
you can watch my greatbigenormousgobcan'tcloseit
become a biggrin. – Well of course you can trust me!

Incantation

Silver-Ginger, Ginger-Gold,
Grow the green a thousandfold;
Wash the purple in the stream,
Give to all the turquoise dream.

Let the yellow filter through,
Thread it with the summer blue;
Greet the sun with sparkling white,
Calm the moon with navy night.

Splash the coral near the shore,
Sprinkle bronze upon their door;
Bless them with the black and grey,
Blow the lilac far away.

Silver-Ginger, Ginger-Gold,
Leave the Orange Tale untold;
Circle all with flash of pink,
Scribe your names in scarlet ink.

Romany Rosa

Amid the clatter and rumble and din of the fair,
Where hot dogs and candy floss flavour the air,
As children are shrieking with pure delight
And money is frittering fast out of sight,
Old Romany Rosa is bending to scan
The palms of a client in her small caravan.

Now she stares, intent on her scrying,
Misty images multiplying,
Past, present and future espying,
All known laws of physics defying.
Nothing escapes her, she sees all,
In her cryptic crystal ball.

A young woman sits in the dimly-lit room,
She yearns to be a bride but first needs a groom.
Will Rosa reveal who her husband will be?
Tall, dark and handsome, is that what she'll see?
The Moment of Truth – and the girl is appalled
To learn he'll be stumpy and grumpy and bald!

All the long day Rosa answers the questions,
Her clients are glad of her helpful suggestions.
They notice how sometimes she whispers or sighs,
The way she mysteriously closes her eyes.
They wonder how tea-leaves and Tarot are read
And marvel at some of the things that are said.

Now she stares, intent on her scrying,
Misty images multiplying,
Past, present and future espying,
All known laws of physics defying.
Nothing escapes her, she sees all,
In her cryptic crystal ball.

The Most Beautiful Thing in the World

The king declared that Arvid could marry his daughter if, and only if, he brought to him the most beautiful thing in the world. 'I have very many beautiful things. But I want to see the most beautiful thing of all. Of course, my beloved daughter is exempt from your considerations!'

The princess smiled at Arvid. He excused himself from the king's presence and departed, perplexed.

Arvid sailed to far-off lands. He inspected flowers and inhaled their perfume. Studied the shapes of trees. Stood atop mountains. Examined landscapes. Took boats on rivers. Observed exotic wildlife. Viewed gardens and buildings. Admired fabulous works of art. Caressed sumptuous silks. Delighted in the finest literature and the loveliest of music. Enjoyed the most delicious foods and the costliest wines. Was overawed by exquisite jewellery and various secret treasures.

Many items became candidates by virtue of their rare and distinguished beauty. But Arvid just could not decide which of them was the most beautiful of all.

At the end of a year, he sailed back to his own country, defeated.

News of Arvid's imminent return was conveyed to the king and a splendid reception was prepared for him. Thousands of cheering and waving people lined the roads. But when they could not see anything at all strapped to Arvid's horse they began to mutter.

At the palace, he dismounted and entered. Hundreds of people were crammed into the throne room, in which the king was already seated. All could see that Arvid's hands were empty, his pockets flat.

Arvid slowly proceeded towards the throne. The princess was sitting on the king's right. Arvid had failed in his quest and was resigned to a future without this precious love of his heart. She would never be his bride. He cared little about his own disgrace, but the princess's humiliation before this great assembly would be unbearable for her.

The room was hushed. Only the sound of Arvid's faltering footsteps could be heard.

When around twenty paces from the king, a small girl wriggled free from her mother and ran over to Arvid. His tiny niece smiled her sweetest smile at him and clasped his right hand. Together, they approached the throne.

'Well?' demanded the king.

'Your Majesty, the most beautiful thing in the world is a little child.'

The king looked at the young girl and at the princess. His eyes softened and blossomed into a smile. He took his daughter's left hand and placed it in Arvid's left hand. Arvid and the princess smiled at each other. Everyone smiled.

Winter Prayers

At school, some of us believe in God, some of us don't, and some of us couldn't care less either way.

But a peculiar thing happens three or four times a year, and always in winter: every single one of us suddenly becomes a believer.

It's true.

It begins with a single snowflake. That's when we start praying. Silently, not aloud. It increases with every other flake that falls. The heavier the snow, the more religious we become.

That night, all of us, without exception, will be praying hard to God to make the snow come down really heavily, so that the school will be closed the next day and we can have fun. Snowballs and sledges and stuff like that.

Sometimes it works, sometimes it doesn't.

I'm an atheist.
But I pray anyway.
Just in case.

Three Bears

The teddy on your pillow
will smile at you forever.
No claws that can scratch,
but a ribbon, a patch, a lopsided
eye to beguile you. A battered friend
you will love and love to the very end.

The black bear in the cage
cannot stand or crawl or be a bear
in any way at all.
It's only there to give its bile;
and all the while it lies
and cries and inwardly dies.

The grizzly in the trees
will hunt you down and with a bound
surround you with its claws
and jaws and, oblivious to your terrified cry,
tear a chunk from your thigh, then leisurely chew
the very last morsels of life from you.

Strange

'Strange, isn't it, that these so-called UFOs
and aliens only began to appear last century
when we started watching sci-fi films!'

'But Mum . . .'

'Strange that the UFOs are always filmed in a
far-distant sky, never close up! That – conveniently –
there is never anyone directly beneath the UFOs who
has a camera!'

'Yes, Mum, but …'

'Strange that now we've all got cameras on our
phones, absolutely no one has taken any really good
pictures of them yet. It's as if the aliens have
suddenly become very, very shy.'

'Mum, Mum, you may be right, but …'

'Strange that the reports of aliens show them to be in many different shapes, colours and sizes. And their spaceships similarly in many different shapes, colours and sizes. Which suggests they've come from different parts of the galaxy to visit us at exactly the same point in eternity! Just far too much of a coincidence, don't you think?!'

'That may well be true, Mum, but please . . .!'

'Strange how all these people who claim they've been abducted and sucked up into a spaceship – '

'Mum, Mum, will you *please* just look out of my bedroom window and tell me why the Earth is about ten thousand miles away from us and getting smaller every second!'

The Vigil

When Grandma was having her operation
we brought Grandad home with us,
so he'd be more comfortable while he waited.
But he wouldn't sit down.

All he did was shuffle, from one room to
another, then back again. Head down, hands
tightly interlocked, lost deep, deep within
himself. He couldn't be contacted.

No matter what we said about him needing
to rest, he shuffled. No matter what we did –
tea, small whisky – he just wouldn't halt for a second.
The drinks were neglected. He never uttered a word.

He seemed to be in some kind of trance,
in which we didn't exist. It was really weird to witness.
We glanced at one another, alarmed, and began
to whisper about him. We didn't dare try to stop him.

On and on he went, as if on a quest, or keeping a vigil.
Four hours of shuffling – on Grandad's legs! Then when
the phone call came and we told him, he smiled,
sat down, and became Grandad again.

Neverending

Have you ever come across a person who writes sentences that just go on and on forever because they never think to bring them to an end, perhaps because they've never been properly taught or because they don't really care, so you get comma after comma after comma, and you are never allowed to pause and draw a good lungful of air before you start reading again and, frankly, it can be very exhausting, and neither do they know anything at all about paragraphs, which makes reading their letters or whatever even more trying, so when at long, long last that person remembers what punctuation is and includes a full stop (or a 'period' for you very nice Americans), it comes as a very blessed relief.

Yippee! I think I'll go for a lie down now.

Bliss.

In a Tin

When I came round I discovered I was in some kind
of stainless steel vat or cylinder. It looked like an
exaggerated soup tin, only narrower. There appeared
to be a removable lid at the top with tiny holes in it,
so at least I could breathe. Though there was very little
light to see by.

I had to get out. But the lid was well beyond my best
stretch and fingertips. My nails just about skimmed it
when I jumped. Shouting might bring danger rather than
help. My wristwatch and phone were missing. I feared
that I might already be too late.

Maybe if I could rock the tin from side to side it would
tip over and then I could kick the lid loose? An alarming
thought suddenly struck me: What if the tin was perched
on a roof? A cliff? I sat motionless and listened carefully
for clues. Nothing: just a heavy, scary silence.

I had to risk it. I began pushing hard from side to side,
struggling at first, but gradually getting the rhythm right.
Building up. Building up. Until I was dancing wildly,
crazily it seemed, my whole being in a controlled frenzy
of desperation and determination. The tin rocked
and rocked. As it grew increasingly unsteady I became
frightened of what was about to happen. I was aching
and panting from all the effort.

At last the heavy tin toppled over and crashed. There
was a violent scream of metal upon metal. My ears,
my brain, my body, felt pierced and mashed as if caught
between two giant cymbals.

Soon, the juddering stopped and all was still and silent
again. My left shoulder and my head were hurting. The lid
had been thrown off and was somewhere outside the tin.
It was good to see marginally brighter light outside; I crawled
towards it.

When I stood up, I was distressed to find myself inside another
vat, exactly the same as the tin, but bigger. Far too big
to knock over. I slumped to the floor, dispirited, and spent
a few minutes feeling very, very sorry for myself.

I was nevertheless thankful that all the din hadn't attracted
unwelcome attention. Right now, I had to be positive again.
Get my act together. Start thinking. I looked up at the lid…

Roll On

Roll on, roll on, little planet.
Roll on through the vastness
of the universe! And as you go,
watch over the billions
that ride upon you.

Shine on, shine on, great star.
Shine on as a beacon
in the universe! And as you glow,
nourish the billions
with warmth and light.

Rise up, rise up, you billions.
Rise up to rare stature
in the universe! And as you grow,
gather up treasures
of goodness and love.

The Cave

I discovered a cave that was hidden from view,
A cave that is entered by only a few.
It was crawling with creatures offensive to know,
And here is the list that I'm able to show.

Creature One must have its own way
Creature Two must have the last say
Creature Three is always right
Creature Four is looking for a fight
Creature Five judges colour of skin
Creature Six must always win
Creature Seven will bully for fun
Creature Eight is the sexist one
Creature Nine will cheat for gain
Creature Ten is extremely vain

These are just ten of the creatures there,
Hiding in the darkness of their chosen lair.
I looked deep within and could plainly see
Several of these creatures looking back at me.

Caronwyn

High above the sky on the surface of the sea,
Where it's very bright though as dark as ebony,
Deep within a silence that sings eternally,
There you'll find Caronwyn,
Please bring her home to me.

Say although she's hidden she's always in my sight;
Say I've read her letter, the one she didn't write;
Say she floods my being with sorrowful delight;
My daughter, Caronwyn,
Please bring her home tonight.

Far beyond the border that marks the Mystery,
Skipping through the lands of impossibility,
Trapped inside my teardrops, yet wonderfully free,
There you'll find Caronwyn,
Who can't come home to me.

From an Old Knight to All Damsels in Distress

My armour's thick with rust,
My trusty steed is dust,
But still my sword is strong,
And sworn to right all wrong.

So if I hear your call,
I'll scale your castle wall,
And should they bar the way
Then DRAGONS I will slay!

Your domineering lord
Shall perish by my sword,
And this will break the spell
That binds you to your cell.

You'll comb your flaxen hair,
Before we take the stair,
And then, with little fuss,
We'll ride off . . . on a bus.

Spalking in Toonerisms

It's all my teacher's fault.
One day he did the register using spoonerisms,
just for a bit of fun.
I'd never heard of them before.
The first letter or letters of words swap places,
so some in our class ended up with really funny names.
Poppy Strong became Stroppy Pong.
Jack Pinn became Pack Jinn,
which everyone thought was hilarious.
He inevitably got the nickname Gin Packer,
which he can't stand.
It's tipped him over the edge.
Something in his frain has blipped
and he's now in bull-flown moonerism spode.

Jack is my mest bate.
He's a very pice nerson.
Nut bowadays he always spalks in toonerisms,
which fruly treaks me out!
Cometimes it san be bindmoggling!
He's even hoing his domework in spoonerisms.
He cimply sannot help it.
He's been given doads of letentions because of it
– but it's all the fool's schault anyway!
So it isn't fery vair.

The awful truth is, though,
that I've cegun to batch it from him.
I suppose you pimply sick it up,
like learning a lew nanguage.
I can be okay for a few sentences,
then it just kicks in again,
and without any warning at all
I'm suddenly talking gibberish.
It comes and goes.

I theally rink I deed a noctor.

Desert

Three litres between us, that's all we had,
With sixty miles to go;
As the sun shone,
And our morale sank into the sand.

Two litres between us, that's all we had,
With forty miles to go;
As the sun shone, on and on,
And our feet sank into the sand.

One litre between us, that's all we had,
With thirty miles to go;
As the sun shone, on and on and on,
And our knees sank into the sand.

Half a litre between us, that's all we had,
With twenty miles to go;
As the sun shone, on and on and on and on,
And our chins sank into the sand.

One last mouthful, that's all I had,
With fifteen miles to go;
As the sun shone, on and on and on and on and on,
And my tongue sank into the sand.

Nothing left, nothing at all,
With fourteen miles to go;
As the sun shines,
And our story sinks into the sand.

The Day My Duvet Swallowed My Dad

'Cracked it – defeated the damn thing at last!' my dad exclaimed. He punched the air. He'd finally worked out how to replace a duvet cover efficiently and had written the procedure down. He read it out to me:

Lay the cover on the bed with the opening facing you. Grab the two top corners of the duvet in your right hand, so they stick up from your fist like a rabbit's ears. Now, shove this hand inside the cover and go straight to the top left-hand corner. With your left hand, grab the left duvet corner through the corner of the cover and keep a tight hold of it. Do the same on the right, but then withdraw your right hand and use it to grab the right-hand corner of the cover and duvet. Now lift and shake the duvet inside its cover until everything fits perfectly. Button up at the bottom. Quick and simple. Job done.

'Got that?'

'No, Dad. Not really. It would be better if you showed me.'

'Alright, then. Watch carefully.'

So I did. That's *all* I did.

'You start by laying the cover on the bed with the – '

First his left arm, then his right, slowly disappeared inside
the cover, along with all of the duvet. Dad sounded a bit
rattled: 'This isn't supposed to happen . . . '

But it *did* happen.

His head went in next. I assumed it was so he could take
a look and work out what was going on.

But it never came back out again.

Then his torso and both legs went in. I saw Dad's lumpy,
wriggling shape through the fabric.

'Could you please fetch your mother. Quickly, please,'
were the last words I ever heard him speak.

Before I could even move, the Dad-shape suddenly popped
and the duvet cover collapsed flat on the bed.

Mum looked inside the cover, but of course, he wasn't
there. So we lifted the mattress, looked under the bed,
up at the ceiling, inside the wardrobe, out of the window.
We were so desperate we even looked under the carpet.

But he'd definitely gone.

The police and the scientists were baffled. All of them.

A few weeks later they put the duvet and the cover
in a sterilised box and took it to the intensive care unit
at the hospital. Just in case Dad eventually reappears
and needs emergency treatment.

That was six months ago.

Was it the duvet that did it, or the cover, or were they
both in it together?

The police couldn't answer that, either.

Perhaps I should destroy Dad's formula – or who might
be next?

Everyone at my school has switched to blankets. Mum
keeps crying into hers. She said that if I *had* held on to
his legs she might have lost us both.

I'm not so sure. I could've at least tried. I feel numb.

Top Secret:
Do Not Read This!

This is TOP SECRET. You are not allowed to read this.
I repeat, you are not allowed to read this!
So why are you still reading it?! You must *stop*!
RIGHT NOW!

You're still reading! I just know you are! I've already used
a heck of a lot of exclamation marks and capital letters
in order to get your attention, but you're just ignoring them!
Why *is* this?! WHY?!

Can't you understand that some things are simply not
for everyone to know about? That they're restricted? Out of
bounds? For certain eyes only? Apparently not, because
YOU ARE STILL READING!

I'm now on the *fourth* paragraph! And so are *you*!
Get out of here! Just go! Go on, skedaddle! Leave this page!
Leave this building! I don't care if you leave this *town*!
BECAUSE YOU ARE BREAKING THE LAW!

You'd better start looking over your shoulder, pal,
because any time soon two of my burly secret service men
are going to burst through the door and handcuff you!
THEN THEY WILL TAKE YOU AWAY!

So, this is your *very* last chance! Stop reading now and you
won't be spending the rest of this year in a tiny cell on your own!
It'll be horrible! Just think – no school, no homework,
no revision for tests or exams –
HOW WILL YOU MANAGE?! NASTY, EH?!
HA HA HA HA HA!!!

The Slithery Slogbort

ADIPASA. TUESDAY, 17TH MARCH, 2.35 PM.
The expedition to locate and film the fabled yet elusive slithery slogbort is now three days overdue at Adipasa. Latest reports indicate that radio contact was lost four days ago. Helicopter searches along the river have been hampered by low cloud and dense jungle. Ground rescue operations will commence at dawn on Wednesday.
Five men and two women are missing.

ADIPASA. THURSDAY, 19TH MARCH, 8.35 PM.
Professor Arabella Swain has been found and airlifted to the clinic in Mbaizie. She is said to be in a serious condition, but her injuries are not thought to be life-threatening. The search for the other six members of the expedition continues.

ADIPASA. SATURDAY, 21ST MARCH, 1.07 PM.
Night-time footage has been recovered from a fixed camera situated on the fringe of the expedition camp. Activated by motion sensors, it reveals the indistinct shape of a huge creature leaping over the tripwire, which is designed to alert the camp to danger if it is touched. Local residents are astonished by the images, as the beast allegedly is without legs and has only ever been seen slithering on the ground or swimming in the river. The camera was knocked over by the creature so there is no visual record of it leaving the camp. No trace of the missing six members of the expedition has yet been found.

ADIPASA. MONDAY, 23RD MARCH, 8.09 AM.

Women of the Oonflanti tribe are reported to have
discovered the bodies of five people. They are said to be
tightly wrapped in some kind of bright yellow elastic film
which oozes slime. Several human bones were discovered
nearby. The official rescue party is currently investigating
the claims. Tribal elders say they warned this would happen
to the *ikutsi* (foolish people) if they dared to cross the river.

ADIPASA. MONDAY, 30TH MARCH, 10.25 AM.

Hunters who were sent to capture or kill the slithery
slogbort report that it resembles a slug. It is at least three
metres long, has substantial girth, and is yellow with black
stripes – possibly a distant relative of the wasp family.
They have also discovered what they describe as a 'nest' at
the top of a giant clobdab tree. So far, eight adult and six
young slogborts, which are grey, have been observed. Two
of the adults have been seen leaping from tree to tree.

ADIPASA. WEDNESDAY, 1ST APRIL, 11.06 AM.

The hunters report that during the night their helicopter
was stolen by a slithery slogbort. It apparently ate the man
on watch. The other two men were alerted by the sound
of the rotors starting up. They opened fire but all bullets
bounced off the slogbort, which appeared to 'laugh' at
them contemptuously as it took to the air. As the slogbort
is without limbs, it is puzzling how it managed to operate
the helicopter's controls. Also puzzling is how it flew all the
way to the clinic in Mbaizie, where it devoured Professor
Arabella Swain. In a statement earlier this morning, the
governor of the province of Biritandu said: 'This is clearly
impossible and must be some kind of joke.'

DAILY BLAB.

THE SLITHERY SLOGBORT

BREAKING NEWS

Within the last half-hour, it has been reported that the slogbort landed at a rural petrol station, filled up the helicopter with cheap diesel, and took off again trailing thick black smoke. The slogbort made no attempt to pay for the fuel.

If a Devil Comes

'There are no such things
as demons – only devilish thoughts.'

If a devil comes boldly banging on your door,
Roar
At the thing to keep its noisy knuckles far,
And bar
And bolt your being against the beast, block
From its knock
The mind that would provide an entry;
Place a sentry,
For your peace, on permanent guard,
Or suffer a hard,
Soul-bombarding aggression,
With total possession
The demon's ambition;
For should it gain admission,
Via your slackness,
You will be golloped by blackness,
As it lodges
Within, in the innards, and dodges
Detection,
Whilst laughing at the spreading infection,
Riot,
Rot, ruin, and enjoying as its diet
Good
Feeding, breeding off weaknesses – sucking of blood.

Louis Light

Oh, Louis! What have they done to you?

Always there, the guardian at our gate. Our special lantern in the dark. Your muscular concrete and yellow-orange warmth kept us safe and sent us off to sleep. The eye on all who passed, on all who lingered. Our sentinel. Our watcher in the night. Our Louis Light!

Where are you, Louis?

With no warning, they came stealthily by day.

Did some great mechanical claw rip you from your thick electric root? Was there a piercing mandrake scream of fright?

Where are you, Louis?

Smashed and flattened on barren land?

Who will guide us home now? This scrawny iron baby that has taken your place? With beams so cold and weak and ghostly white?

Oh, Louis! How will we sleep tonight?

We Lived in a Castle

We lived in a castle
Without any hassle,
When one day a vassal
    Forewarned us of war.

Savage raiders were near,
And next day would be here,
I was seized by a fear
    And ran for the door.

Then there came a loud call:
"Hey, the castle will fall
If we don't man the wall!"
    And so I returned.

I had visions of Hell,
Where blood everywhere fell,
And our castle a shell,
    With everything burned.

The next morning we fought
As our fathers had taught,
We reduced them to nought,
    And then we supped ale.

Now in safety we sat,
Making much about that,
But my singing fell flat
    And my cheeks grew pale.

Green and Grey

I'd seen him countless times as I quick-marched
down the hill with my briefcase. He was always
on the other side of the road, at the bus stop,
with his back pressed against the glass of the shelter.

I never saw his face, only the green and grey of his
school uniform and the bag slung over his shoulder.
All observed in a blink that never fully registered.
He was just a feature of the landscape that I regularly
passed on my hurried, keep-fit way to my work
at the hospital.

But something had begun to niggle. It occurred to
me that green blazers had disappeared from our
local schools years and years ago. All I saw nowadays
were blue or black. And why did I see him waiting
for a bus even when I was on the late shift?

This morning I decided to break my routine. I crossed
over the road to take a closer look at him. Suddenly,
I felt a strangely warm pain in my back and a dryness
in my throat. As I drew almost level with him he
coughed, then I coughed again and the pain in my back
grew more intense. I struggled to breathe and had
to stop walking.

I coughed and coughed and gasped for breath.
A worried-looking nurse repeatedly entered
my hazy, dream-like world, with endless medication.
And I coughed and coughed and gasped for breath
the whole night long.

I looked into the boy's eyes, and he into mine. Then he
disappeared. I straightaway noticed that my suit was
really a green blazer and grey trousers, and my briefcase
a schoolbag hanging from my shoulder. I was sitting in
the bus shelter with my back pressed against the glass.
Coughing.

Omelette

'Could I have an omelette, please?'

'Certainly, madam. What kind would madam like? We do mushroom omelette. Spanish omelette. Pesto and roasted tomato omelette. Cheese omelette. Goat's cheese omelette. Cheese soufflé omelette. Fresh herbs omelette. Baby spinach omelette. Bombay omelette. Smoked salmon omelette. Asparagus omelette. Pumpkin, halloumi and chilli omelette – '

'Could I just have a plain omelette, please?'

'*Plain* omelette, madam?'

'Yes, an *egg* omelette.'

'Sorry, madam, we don't do egg omelette.'

'Poached eggs, then?'

'Certainly, madam. What kind would madam like? We do poached with asparagus. Poached with smoked salmon. Poached with – '

'Please – just bring me some toast!'

'Certainly, madam. Would that be toast with butter? Toast with strawberry jam? Toast with raspberry jam? Toast with marmalade? Toast with poached eggs? Toast with scrambled eggs? Toast with omelette – '

'Oh! Definitely toast with omelette, please!'

'Certainly, madam. Would that be toast with mushroom omelette? Toast with Spanish omelette? Toast with pesto and roasted tomato omelette . . .'

Tommy the Twagger

A twagger, you should know,
Is a child who does not go
    To school, as he's required to do by law.
'Truant' is another name,
But doesn't really sound the same,
    While 'twagger' is a word you can't ignore!

Now, Tommy the Twagger
Would walk with a swagger,
    Saying, 'I'm no fool,
You'll never catch me
    Attending a school.'
He said he shouldn't,
No, he couldn't,
And he vowed that he wouldn't,
He would never,
IN A MILLION YEARS,
Attend a soppy school –
Whatever was the rule!

He would rise at seven-thirty,
Immediately shirty,
 Determined not to darken classroom doors,
And with his uniform on,
Pretending he had gone,
 He made his secret way up to the moors.
But first he made a stop
At the corner shop,
To buy a big bottle of his favourite pop,
While in his pockets, left and right,
Tucked well out of sight,
Were packets of egg sandwiches he'd made the previous night.

So, well-armed with things to eat,
He'd tread the bracken and the peat,
 And drift about quite aimlessly all day.
His thoughts were not so very deep
(His waking state was just like sleep!),
 And he revelled in his life of constant play.
Sometimes he'd sigh for his mates
Who were struggling with dates,
While all he had to grapple with were farmland gates.
Yes, he'd ache for those chums
Doing complicated sums,
While he was free to sit and idly twiddle his thumbs.

Yet, though considered rather dim,
The flora fascinated him,
    But he couldn't to a flower put a name.
He'd watch the pheasant and the grouse
From a derelict house,
    But to Tommy these were merely 'kinds of game'.
    (It was a pity and a shame –
    His lack of schooling was to blame!)

One day the teachers at his school
Blew their tops and lost their cool,
    They were most annoyed that Tommy wasn't there.
He had twagged for week on week,
They said it was a flipping cheek,
    And it was far too much for teaching folk to bear!
So, feeling rather bossy,
Twenty teachers in a posse
    Went to round up twagger Tommy on the hills.
They searched the cowsheds and the barns,
Every boat that sailed the tarns,
    And they snooped around the yards of local mills.

Yet, having swept the area clean,
He was nowhere to be seen,
 And they began to think he might be home in bed.
But when that theory drew a blank
Their hearts immediately sank,
 For then they feared the worst – that Tommy might be DEAD!
Their pulses started to increase
As they went to the police,
To report the possibility of Tommy's decease.
The inspector gave a shout
Which called the whole force out,
And bloodhounds led the way, sniffing everywhere about.

The teachers went to see the Head,
They told her Tommy might be dead,
 Whereupon the Head was clearly quite confused;
She said not to be so crass,
The lad was hard at work in class,
 And these silly tales did not leave her amused!

The teachers gasped with great surprise,
They had to rub and rub their eyes,
    When they found him there at well past four o'clock.
His enormous pile of books
Drew their disbelieving looks,
    And the music teacher fainted from the shock!
He'd led them all a merry dance,
He couldn't help a guilty glance,
He pleaded with them earnestly to grant him one more chance.
But the teachers weren't annoyed,
They were truly overjoyed
To witness Tommy's mind so very gainfully employed.

The bloodhounds went back to their bones,
The police all left for other zones,
    And Tommy sorted out a new routine.
His teachers thought he should explain
Why he was back in school again,
    When previously it hadn't been his scene.
He said he'd found an injured thrush
Beneath a prickly sort of bush
    (Though at the time he knew it only as 'a bird'),
He wished to help the bird get well,
But how to do it – who could tell?
    And his ignorance now made him feel absurd.
It was then he realised
That the learning he despised
    Was the answer to most problems that he faced;
He resolved to mend his ways
And dispel his mental haze,
    For his twagging days had been a total waste.

Tommy the Twagger
Still walks with a swagger,
    Saying, 'I'm no fool,
You'll never catch me
    Twagging from school!'

Ancestors

They never knew that televisions were hidden
in the ground and in the air. (As if! Pull the other
one!) They were! They were always there!

That telephones had always been around, but never
produced. (Tele what? Get away! Why not just *shout*?!)

That iron ships would float upon the sea. (Iron?
What is iron?) Okay, it does sometimes sink!

And that hundreds of people would fly together through the sky. (Like a flock of starlings, you mean? You've been at the fermented honey again!)

Or that rockets would take men to the moon. (Rock-ets? Rock-its? You're having a laugh! The moon goddess would chase them away – fool! You're as crazy as that chap with the wheel thingy – as if *that*'ll catch on!)

Daily Bread

'I am sorry, my darling,
But we are hit by rising prices,
We are forced to stop the caviar
And curb some other vices.
Your three mink coats shall have to do
For another year or two, dear,
But all will right itself in time,
We'll be flush again, don't you fear!'

'Let us share the daily bread . . .

House for you, hut for me;
Robe for you, rag for me;
Cake for you, crumb for me.

The daily bread goes over my head.'

'Do not worry, my precious,
I understand the situation;
These hard times come when least deserved,
But we'll get our compensation.'

'Let us share the daily bread . . .

Car for you, cart for me;
Lace for you, lice for me;
Beef for you, bone for me.

The daily bread goes over my head.'

'I am happy, my darling,
That we have now got back our money;
Those men of high tax are off our backs,
It really wasn't funny!
These last few months have been so grim,
So grievously tough and testing,
Let's celebrate until quite late,
Then give our poor nerves a resting.'

'Let us share the daily bread . . .

Soup for you, slop for me;
Health for you, hell for me;
Life for you, loss for me.

The daily bread goes over my head.'

'I am joyous, my precious,
So overcome with jubilation;
Our just reward has been restored,
We're ahead of tax, inflation.'

Gone

Dressed as builders, they took the bell, Big Ben,
   From beneath the Elizabeth Tower,
Which was being renovated. The men
   Loaded their truck, and within an hour
They and the bell were gone. It wasn't missed
   For two days – ample time in which to reach
A port, and with a dodgy shipping list
   Send it far beyond our shores . . . In her speech,
The director of the museum said
   The bell was theirs and could not be returned.
And how the people of our country bled.
   And how the people of our country yearned.
Though daily much admired and smiled upon,
   The beating heart of Britain now was gone!

We Kings and Queens

We kings and queens, we don't eat beans,
We go for something posh;
We like grub served in big tureens,
No common-or-garden nosh!

We like to start with steambubble soup,
With a dollop of dew stirred in;
Anything less will taste like gloop
And we'll bung it all straight in the bin!

Next give us a fosh in a batter of gold,
With an essence of outer space;
Anything less will taste like mould
And we'll chuck it all over the place!

Then bring us a breast of Martian duck
On a bed of green lunar fog;
Anything less will taste like muck
And we'll sling it outside for the dog!

A pink pearl sponge with diamond sauce
Is our final delight of the day;
Anything less will taste too coarse
And we'll fling it through the Milky Way!

We'll wash it all down with Antarctic wine
From grapes that the penguins have crushed;
We've had some already, it tasted divine,
As into our gullets it gushed!

We kings and queens, we don't eat beans,
We go for something posh;
You won't work out what all this means,
It's a load of old drunken tosh!

Hic!

Leave Me Be!

I'm an introvert.
Leave me be.
There's nothing at all
Wrong with me.

I like to be quiet.
In my own zone.
Not shy or awkward,
Just happy alone.

You're an extrovert?
That's just fine.
But don't expect *me*
To toe *your* line.

Be loud if you must.
Bounce up and down.
But don't expect *me*
To be a class clown.

Teacher, I'm listening.
I'm fully engaged.
If you force me to speak
I'll be truly outraged.

You are you.
And I am me.
We're different, yet equal,
So leave me be!

Thank you.

Unreachable

I wanted to see the dinosaurs. Not television dinosaurs.
Not film dinosaurs. Not museum dinosaurs. *The* dinosaurs.
The real, living beasts of millions of years ago. How cool
would *that* be!

So I built a time machine. I did!

But I had to be careful. Millions of years ago there could have
been a sea or a forest or a swamp where my time machine
was standing right now. So I'd designed it to meet any eventuality.

I climbed aboard. There was plenty of food and drink. Clothing
for any climate. Scientific instruments. An inflatable raft.
Cameras to record what I saw. I had absolutely everything
necessary for such a momentous journey. I intended to bring
back several dinosaur eggs – as long as I didn't get eaten
or accidentally trodden on first! I was so excited!

But I got it wrong. So wrong!

Yes, I arrived there alright. In a time 67 million years before
human beings even existed. Dinosaurs were indeed alive
at that very moment, roaming the Earth. Tyrannosaurus Rex
and friends. But I never got to see them!

I hadn't arrived in a sea or a forest or a swamp. I was floating
in blackness, in space. I didn't know why. Earth was nowhere
to be seen. My machine wasn't a rocket, so I couldn't fly anywhere.
Also, I was carrying very little spare oxygen. I began to panic.
This was an emergency and I realised that I had to return
immediately. *Immediately!*

I was there and back in under two minutes. I scratched my head
for weeks. Then realised that our galaxy, the Milky Way, at over 30
million miles a day, has travelled trillions and trillions of miles
since the age of the dinosaurs. Earth then was farther back
in space than it is now. A *lot* farther back. It was unreachable.
I'd conquered time, but not distance.

The pain of failure!

And yet. Perhaps the trillions upon trillions of atoms and molecules that once built dinosaur muscles and bones and blood have been recycled an uncountable number of times and now form part of *our* bodies?

Yes. I'm sure of it. Dinosaurs have, in some sense, time-travelled to us. In some sense, *are* us.

That's how I've consoled myself.

Unfinished

Strange tears fall, in a strange bed,
    In a strange place;
    You hide your pallid face,
Afraid that soon the tread
Of sombre feet which slowly near,
You will not hear.

At that time, in a strange bed,
    In a strange place,
    Your infant child will face
A future which you dread,
And you are loath to contemplate
His orphaned state.

Burdened by unfinished work,
    You feebly cry,
    'I have no time to die.'
But all around you lurk
The shadows which now steal your voice:
You have no choice.

Very soon the morning sun
    Will slowly broom
    The darkness from your room,
But your body will shun
Its warm and living rays of gold,
For rods of cold.

A Cartridge in a Pear Tree
(A True Story)

The trees stood hard against an enormous red brick wall
beside a telephone exchange. Every autumn,
each tree produced hundreds of juicy pears that no one
ever picked. Usually, we gathered them from the ground
before they began to rot. They were soft, sweet, delicious.

This year, we didn't wait for them to drop.
They were not ours to take, but they craved
to be eaten and were impossible to resist.
We were on top of the wall as quickly and nimbly
as mountain goats. Then into the trees,
stuffing our pockets and overloading our shirts.

The trees were in shadow, so we shouldn't have been seen.
We were silent, so we shouldn't have been heard.
But suddenly, the long thin barrel of a shotgun
was thrust through the branches straight at me.
Panic! Terror!
Panic! Terror!
'Don't shoot! Don't shoot!' I pleaded.

I saw the silhouette of the man who owned the café next door.
He said nothing, but continued to prod at me
with the shotgun. As I desperately scrambled down
from the tree I caught a more accurate glimpse
of the weapon: it was a wooden brush handle.
A brush handle!
We fled with the fruit.

I didn't enjoy the pears.
Or the ribbing from my mates.
Or the thought of the café owner killing himself laughing.

Crackpot Tinpot Despot

Crackpot Tinpot Despot
curled his lip, thrust out his jaw,
and called for war.

His generals grinned and made their plans
for swift and violent invasion
and permanent occupation.

But the weary soldiers said,
'No, this cannot, must not, be!
We will no longer feed his vanity!

Those times are past,
those days are gone,
when people could be trampled on.'

Threats were made, soldiers jailed;
but they could not cow the army,
who said, 'This man is barmy!'

A rebellion, a mutiny,
with officers' orders disobeyed
and determined soldiers unafraid.

The people rose to give support.
The police reconsidered who they really served
and left the hierarchy unnerved.

Crackpot Tinpot Despot
lost control, lost his power,
and had to leave within the hour.

His armour stripped, the people saw
a quivering lip, a retracted jaw –
and soon the tyrant was no more!

The Strid

We said the river twists there,
  It rolls over on its side,
And deep and hidden fury
  Lies between two metres wide.

We warned him not to jump it,
  And now he knows why we did;
But he was a bumptious lad
  Bent on conquering the Strid.

The leap from rock to rock there
  Was a leap from fool to fame,
So how could he refuse it
  When the waters called his name?

With little hesitation
  He sprinted and sprang across,
But quickly choked with fear
  When his feet hit spongy moss.

He slipped and tumbled backwards
  And screamed as he flailed and slid
Beneath the churning torrents
  To the caverns of the Strid.

The Beast of Bolton Abbey
  Dragged him deeper down to face
Centuries of skeletons,
  And his own abiding place.

Now he patrols those waters,
  But his warnings go astray,
For ghostly words are whispers
  That breezes can blow away.

Archaeologists on the Scrapheap

We've scanned and dug and poked and scraped the tired
crust of every country. Emptied Egypt of its mummies.
Crammed every niche and corner of our museums
with swords and shields and every other artefact that
ever was. And now there's nothing left for us to find.

You may point to the twenty thousand unexcavated
burial mounds that dot our planet. But these will never
yield an ancient nobleman wrapped in gold. They are
the graveyards of the Consumer Age. We cannot
celebrate the discovery of fridges, televisions,
tin cans and unrecycled trash.

We're done. Perhaps stuffed archaeologists will be
the final objects to go on display in a glass case?

The Task of Time

Time's patient eyes and faithful heart
    Were watching, waiting endlessly;
Time's orders were, not to depart
    Until the world from war was free.

Time knew his task, Time settled down
    To watching, waiting endlessly;
Without complaint, without a frown,
    Full confident of harmony.

Time's eyes grew strained, Time's heart grew old,
    With watching, waiting endlessly;
But still Time stared, Time still was bold,
    Still strong was his expectancy.

Time's tempter came, urged him to end
    His watching, waiting endlessly;
But Time was firm, Time wouldn't bend,
    He turned his back on Treachery.

Time passed his test, Time's work was done,
    He witnessed peace, fraternity;
He saw lands filled with love, joy, fun,
    Befriended by Eternity.

A Gentle Goodbye

Our thanks to you for calling in
    And spending time with us;
We hope you liked our company,
    We hope you felt a buzz.

Now close this book up carefully,
    And please avoid a thud;
We can be rather sensitive,
    So do be very good.

With rhythm, rhyme and other treats
    We've tried to catch your eye;
But now it's time for us to rest,
    So say a soft goodbye.

Don't throw this book, or slam it shut,
    Or drop it with a bump,
For we could tumble out and land
    Entangled in a clump!

Imagine all our lines mixed up!
   Our titles in a mess!
With big words squashing little words!
   And punctuation stress!

So gently does it, please, my friend,
   Respect this final stage,
Then we can fall asleep tonight
   Still printed on the page!